ScienceMats

Including Science PlaceMats™, Science ThinkMats™, and Unit Assessment

Solids, Liquids, and Gases

States of Matter and How They Change

DEVELOPED IN COOPERATION
WITH
NEW YORK HALL OF SCIENCE
CORONA, NEW YORK

Scholastic Inc. grants teachers who have purchased the Scholastic Science Place™ ScienceMats for *Solids, Liquids, and Gases* permission to reproduce Science PlaceMats™ and Science ThinkMats™ from this book for use in their classrooms. Notice of copyright must appear on all copies of Science PlaceMats™ and Science ThinkMats™
Science PlaceMats™ and Science ThinkMats™ are trademarks of Scholastic Inc.

Copyright © 1993 by Scholastic Inc.   All rights reserved. Published by Scholastic Inc.   Printed in the U.S.A.
ISBN 0-590-26252-1
8 9 10   33   99 98 97 96

Contents

Solids, Liquids, and Gases

What Are Scientists?

A scientist asks questions and tries different ways to answer them.

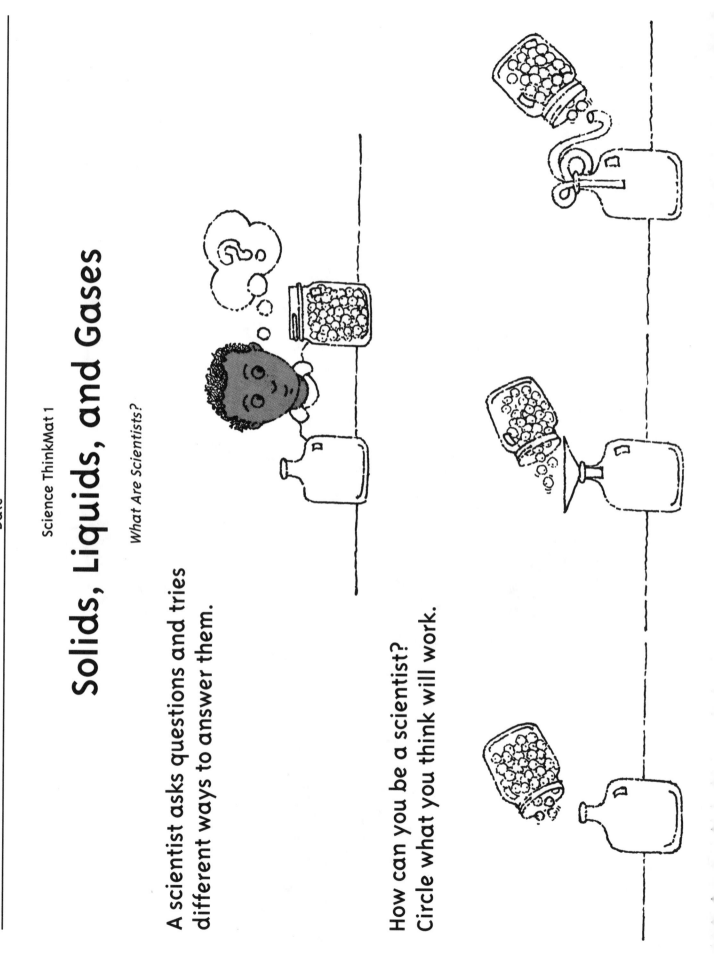

How can you be a scientist?
Circle what you think will work.

Name _____   Date _____

Why Does Matter Matter?

1. Look. Find matter.

Draw or write about what you found out. ✏️

Name

Date

Why Does Matter Matter?

Draw a picture of something that is matter.

Circle the sentences that tell how you know what you drew is matter.

A. It takes up space.

B. I can see it.

C. I can taste it.

D. I can feel it.

E. I can smell it.

Science PlaceMat 3

Can You Name the Matter?

Draw or write about what you found out.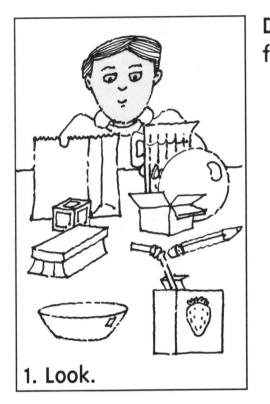

1. Look.

2. Test.

Science ThinkMat 3

Can You Name the Matter?

Solve the riddle. Circle the answer.

I change shape easily.
Pour me into a glass, and I will become that shape.

  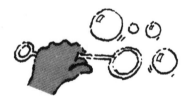

If the window is open, I leave.
I can float.

  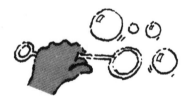

If I fall on the floor,
you can easily pick me up.

Science PlaceMat 4

What Are Solids?

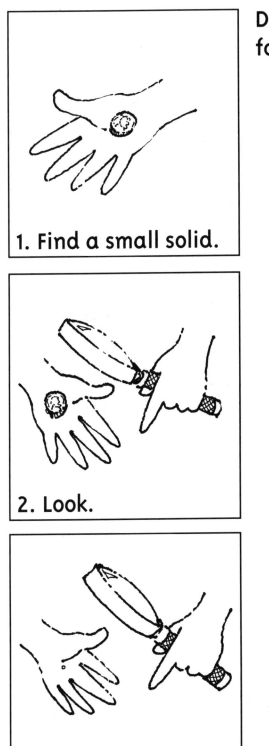

1. Find a small solid.

2. Look.

3. Look at salt.

Draw or write about what you found out.

Science ThinkMat 4

What Are Solids?

Color and cut.
Place cards face down.
Pick a card. Describe it.
Ask your friend if it is a
solid.

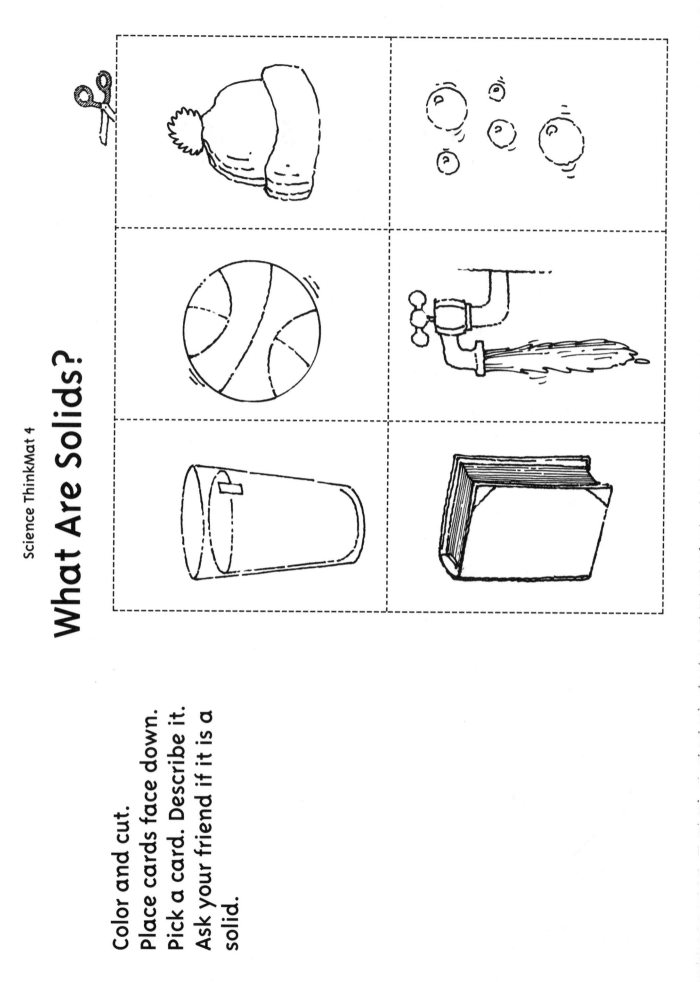

Science PlaceMat 5

What Are Liquids?

Draw or write about what you found out.

1. Pour beads.
   Observe.

2. Pour water.
   Observe.

Science ThinkMat 5

What Are Liquids?

Find the shortest path to the container
of juice with the same shape.

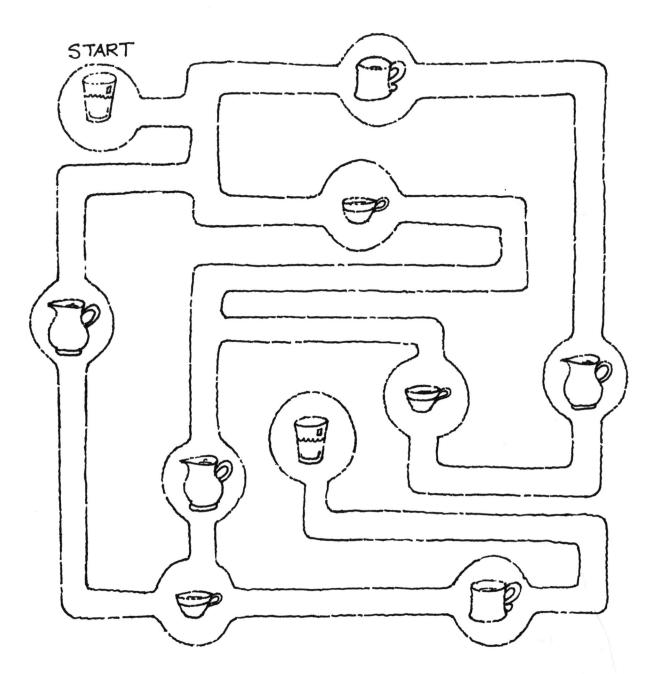

Science PlaceMat 6

What Are Gases?

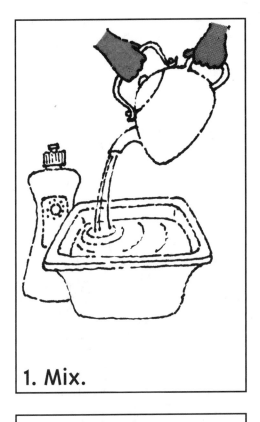

1. Mix.

Draw or write about what you found out.

2. Predict. Blow.

What Are Gases?

Circle the gases in the picture.

Science ThinkMat 7

Changes, Changes

1. Mix dirt and water.   Draw or write about what happens.

2. Make a pie.

3. Bake the pie.

  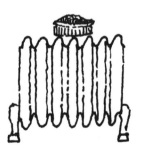

Draw or write about what happens.

What Happens to Solids in Liquids?

1. Fill. Add salt. Add sand.

2. Stir. Wait.

3. Pour. Observe.

Draw or write about what you found out.

Science ThinkMat 8

What Happens to Solids in Liquids?

Color and cut. Paste the objects where they belong.

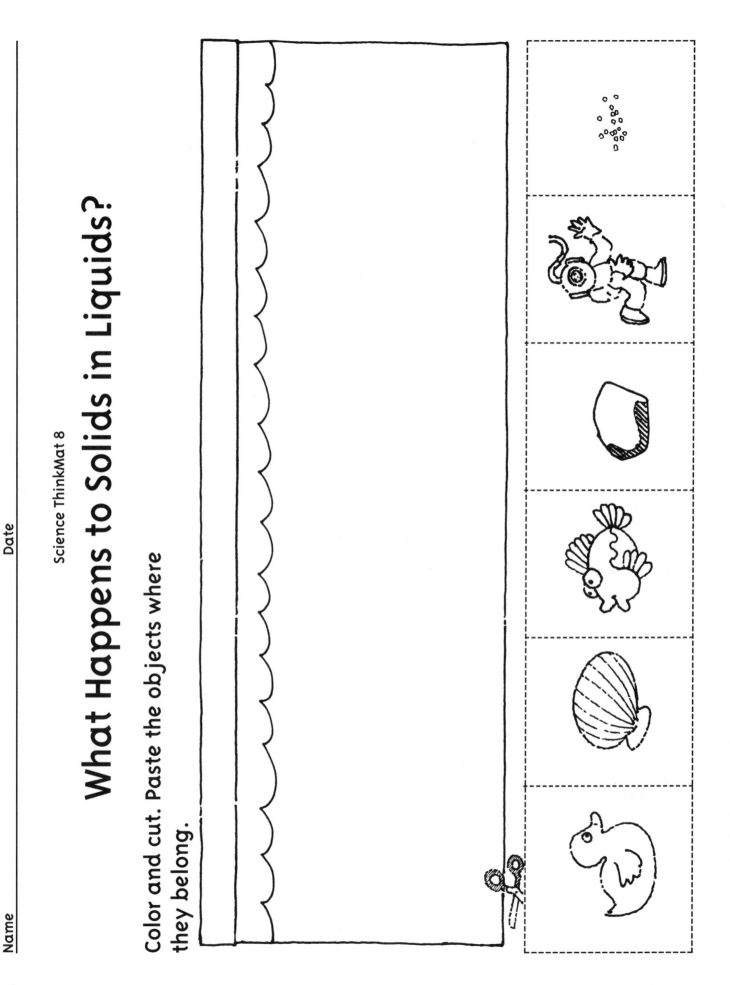

Science PlaceMat 9

What Happens to Liquids in Liquids?

1. Mix. Cover and shake.

2. Add oil. Cover. Turn.

3. Shake. Observe.

Draw or write about what you found out.

Science ThinkMat 9

What Happens to Liquids in Liquids?

Draw pictures to show what you can do with these mixed liquids.

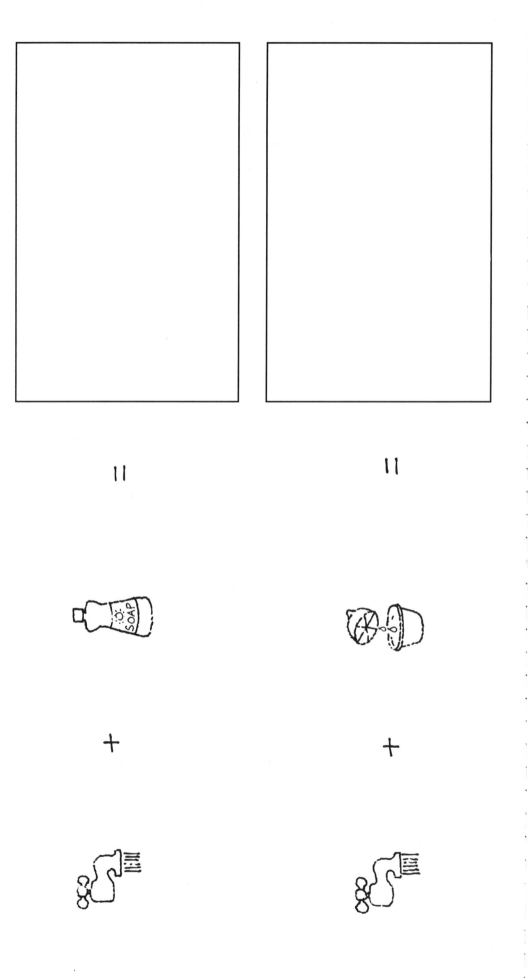

What Happens to Gases in Liquids?

Draw or write about what you found out.

1. Blow up. Let go.

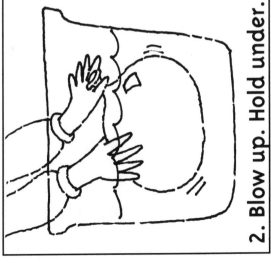

2. Blow up. Hold under.

Science ThinkMat 10

What Happens to Gases in Liquids?

Circle the pictures that show gases in liquids.

Science PlaceMat 11

How Small Can It Get?

Draw or write about what you found out.

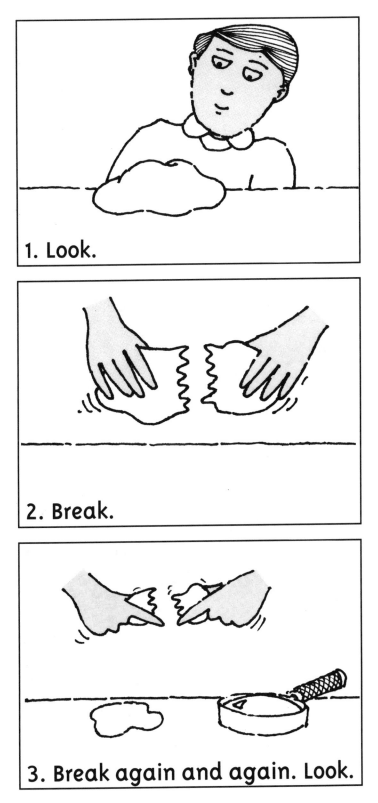

1. Look.

2. Break.

3. Break again and again. Look.

Science ThinkMat 11

How Small Can It Get?

Is it still the same matter?

Yes   No

Yes   No

Yes   No

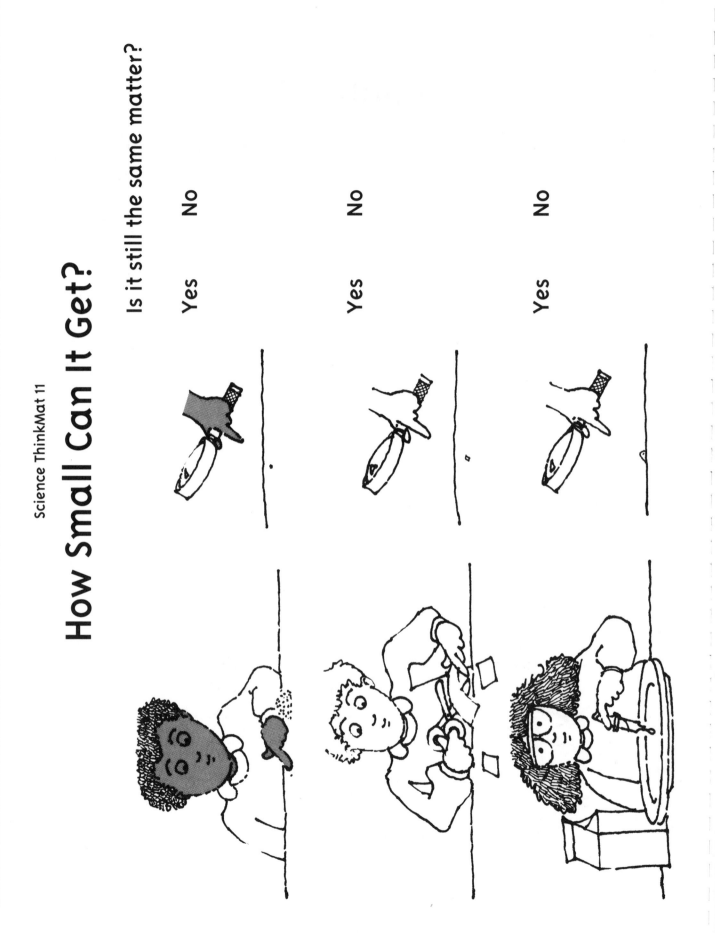

What Is Matter Made Of?

**Look at each picture. What kind of matter is it?
Circle the answer.**

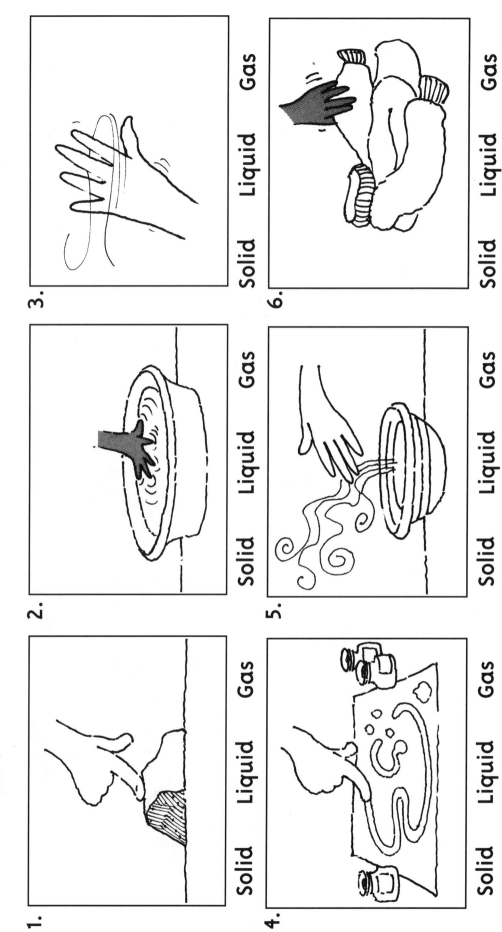

1.
Solid   Liquid   Gas

2.
Solid   Liquid   Gas

3.
Solid   Liquid   Gas

4.
Solid   Liquid   Gas

5.
Solid   Liquid   Gas

6.
Solid   Liquid   Gas

Name

Date

Science PlaceMat 13

How Can You Change a Solid to a Liquid?

Draw or write about what you found out.

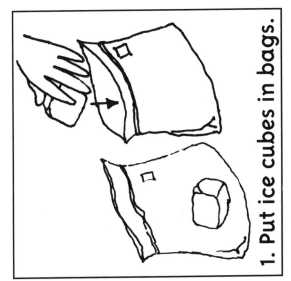

1. Put ice cubes in bags.

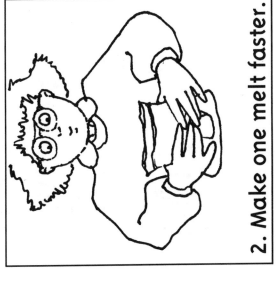

2. Make one melt faster.

How Can You Change a Solid to a Liquid?

Cut out the pictures at the bottom of the page.
Paste them in the boxes to show what happens.

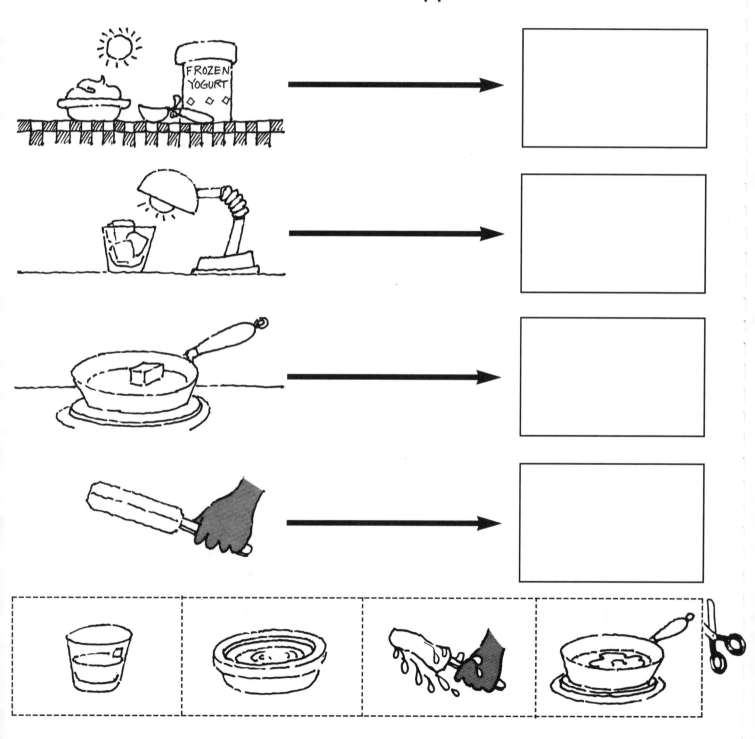

More to come.

Science ThinkMat 14

How Is a Crayon Made?

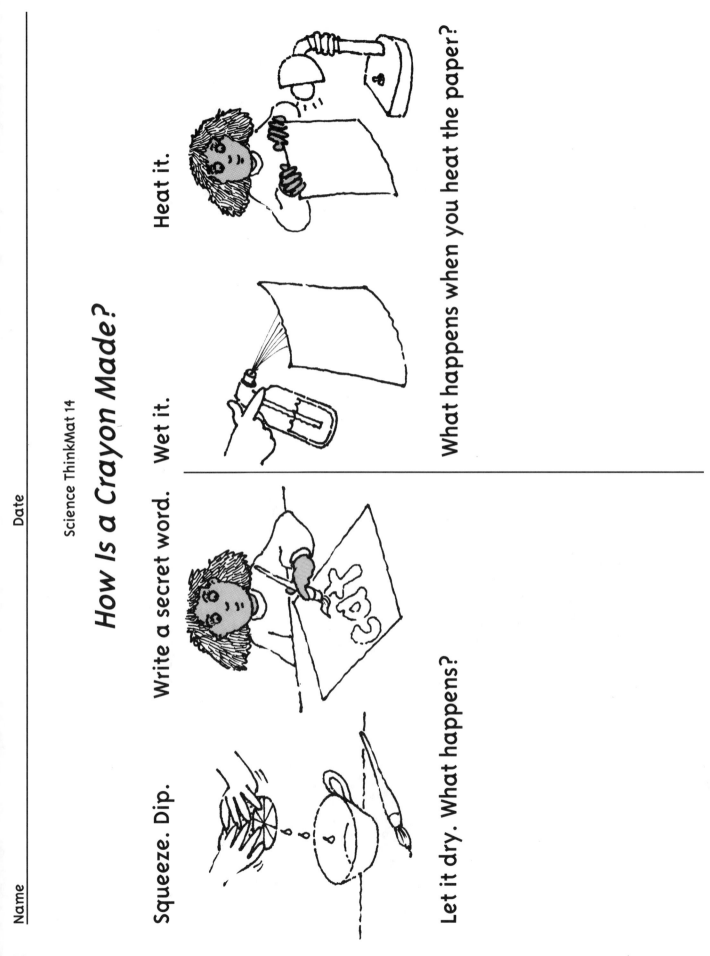

Squeeze. Dip.

Write a secret word.

Wet it.

Heat it.

Let it dry. What happens?

What happens when you heat the paper?

How Can You Change a Solid and a Liquid to a Gas?

Draw or write about what you found out.

1. Pour.

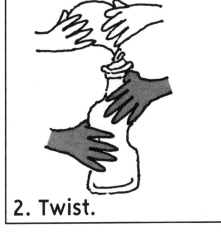

2. Twist.

3. Lift and untwist.

How Can You Change a Solid and a Liquid to a Gas?

Put in yeast. Add warm water. Stir.

Pour into 2 cups.

Add sugar to one cup. Stir.

Put cups in a warm place.

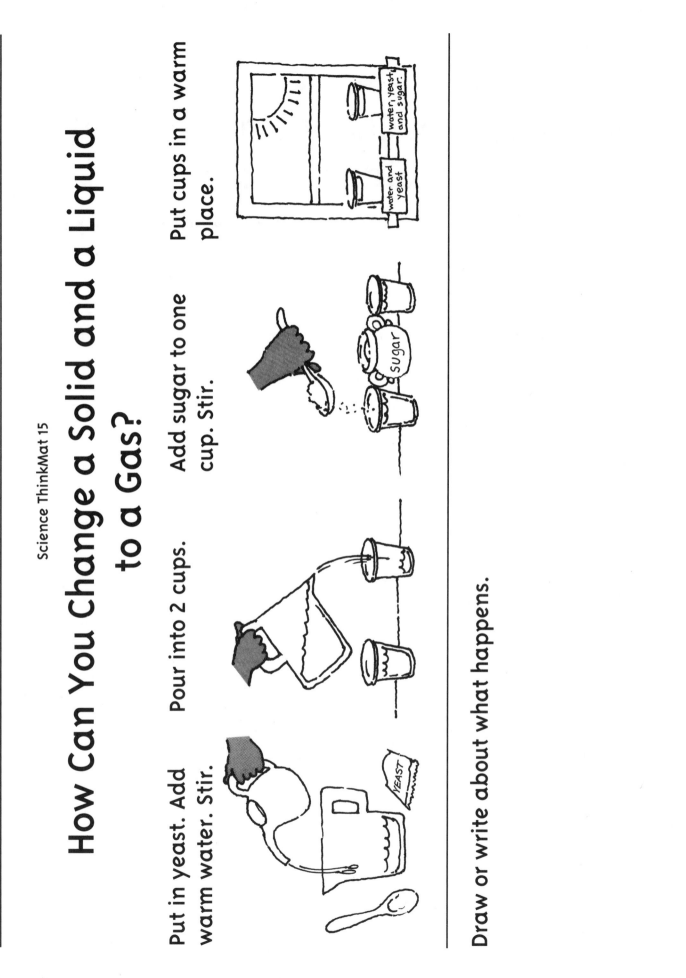

Draw or write about what happens.

Scholastic Science Place   *Solids, Liquids, and Gases*   Science ThinkMat 15

Check out the next page.

Science ThinkMat 16

What Makes Matter Change?

Look at each picture. What happens when fire
or heat is added? Draw or write what you think.

Where Can You Find Changing Matter?

1. Mix. Add.

2. Feel. Press into ball.

3. Spread out.

Draw or write about what you found out.

Where Can You Find Changing Matter?

Color the matter that is changing. Then
put a ◯ around the solids, a ▢ around
the liquids, and a △ around the gases.

Science PlaceMat 18

Bag Some Matter

Draw or write about what you did.

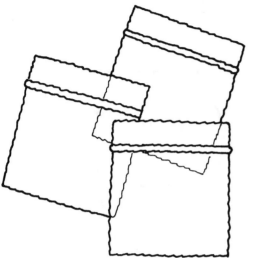

Science ThinkMat 18

What Did We Learn?

Circle the best answer.

1. Which is a solid?

2. Which takes the shape of its container?

      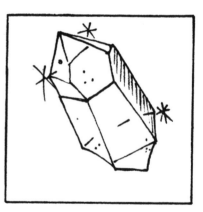

3. Circle the shape that shows matter changing form to another.

Name _____   Date _____

Science ThinkMat 2

Why Does Matter Matter?

Draw a picture of something that is matter.

Circle the sentences that tell how you know what you drew is matter.

A. It takes up space.

B. I can see it.

C. I can taste it.

D. I can feel it.

E. I can smell it.

Circled sentences should always include A.

Name _____   Date _____

Science ThinkMat 1

Solids, Liquids, and Gases

What Are Scientists?

A scientist asks questions and tries different ways to answer them.

How can you be a scientist?
Circle what you think will work.

Name _____ Date _____

Science ThinkMat 4

What Are Solids?

Color and cut.
Place cards face down.
Pick a card. Describe it.
Ask your friend if it is a
solid.

*As children describe
objects, encourage them to
give clues such as: whether
the object can change
shape on its own; what it
feels like to touch; what
happens if it is dropped.*

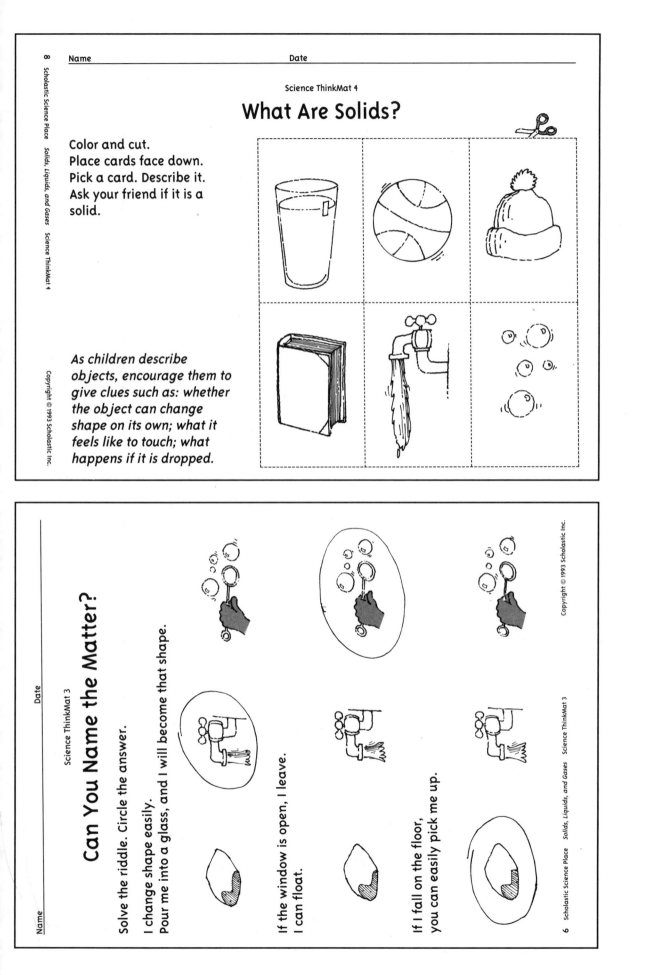

Name _____ Date _____

Science ThinkMat 3

Can You Name the Matter?

Solve the riddle. Circle the answer.

I change shape easily.
Pour me into a glass, and I will become that shape.

If the window is open, I leave.
I can float.

If I fall on the floor,
you can easily pick me up.

Science ThinkMat 6

What Are Gases?

Circle the gases in the picture.

Science ThinkMat 5

What Are Liquids?

Find the shortest path to the container of juice with the same shape.

START

T–3

Name _____   Date _____

Scholastic Science Place   *Solids, Liquids, and Gases*   Science ThinkMat 8

Science ThinkMat 8

What Happens to Solids in Liquids?

Color and cut. Paste the objects where they belong.

Children should glue the duck on top of the water, the fish swimming around in the water, the shell and the rock on the bottom. The diver may be suspended in water or at bottom; sand will be at bottom of water and/or in suspension.

Name _____   Date _____

Science ThinkMat 7

Changes, Changes

1. Mix dirt and water.   Draw or write about what happens.

It makes mud.

2. Make a pie.

3. Bake the pie.

Draw or write about what happens.

It becomes hard and dry.

14   Scholastic Science Place   *Solids, Liquids, and Gases*   Science ThinkMat 7

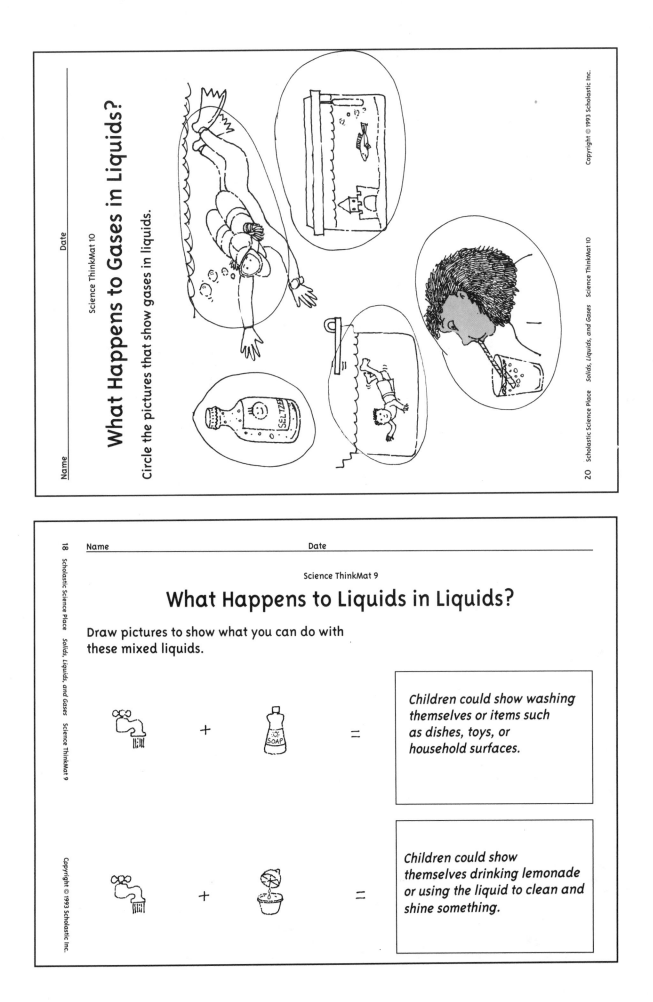

What Happens to Gases in Liquids?

Circle the pictures that show gases in liquids.

SELTZER

What Happens to Liquids in Liquids?

Draw pictures to show what you can do with
these mixed liquids.

SOAP

+   =

*Children could show washing
themselves or items such
as dishes, toys, or
household surfaces.*

+   =

*Children could show
themselves drinking lemonade
or using the liquid to clean and
shine something.*

Name _____   Date _____

Science ThinkMat 12

What Is Matter Made Of?

Look at each picture. What kind of matter is it?
Circle the answer.

1.

Solid Liquid Gas
(Solid circled)

2.

Solid Liquid Gas
(Liquid circled)

3.

Solid Liquid Gas
(Gas circled)

4.

Solid Liquid Gas
(Liquid circled)

5.

Solid Liquid Gas
(Gas circled)

6.

Solid Liquid Gas
(Solid circled)

Name _____   Date _____

Science ThinkMat 11

How Small Can It Get?

Is it still the same matter?

Yes   No
_____

Yes   No
_____

Yes   No
_____

All answers are yes.

Name _____ Date _____

Science ThinkMat 14

How Is a Crayon Made?

Squeeze. Dip.　　**Write a secret word.**　　**Wet it.**　　**Heat it.**

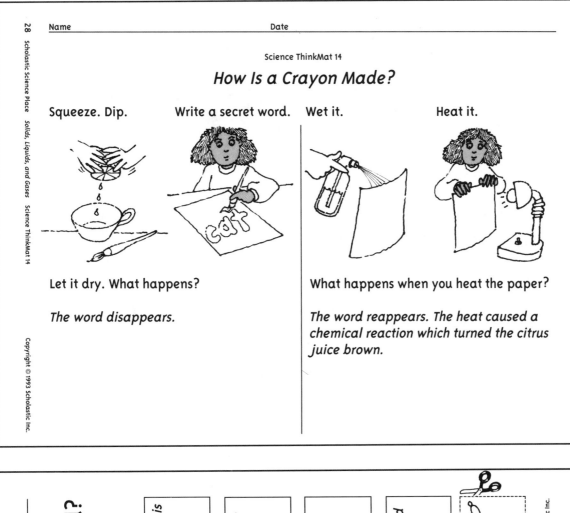

Let it dry. What happens?

The word disappears.

What happens when you heat the paper?

The word reappears. The heat caused a chemical reaction which turned the citrus juice brown.

Name _____ Date _____

Science ThinkMat 13

How Can You Change a Solid to a Liquid?

Cut out the pictures at the bottom of the page.
Paste them in the boxes to show what happens.

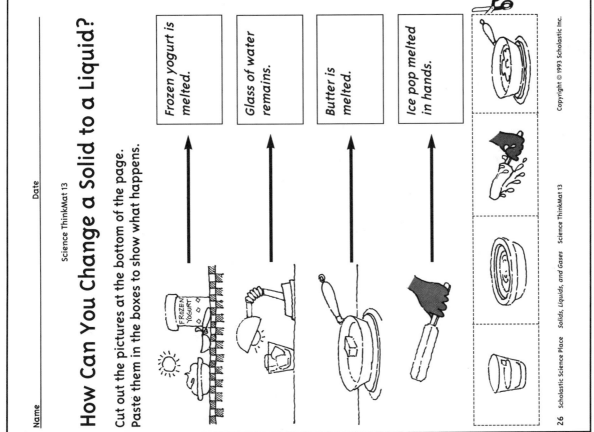

Frozen yogurt is melted.

Glass of water remains.

Butter is melted.

Ice pop melted in hands.

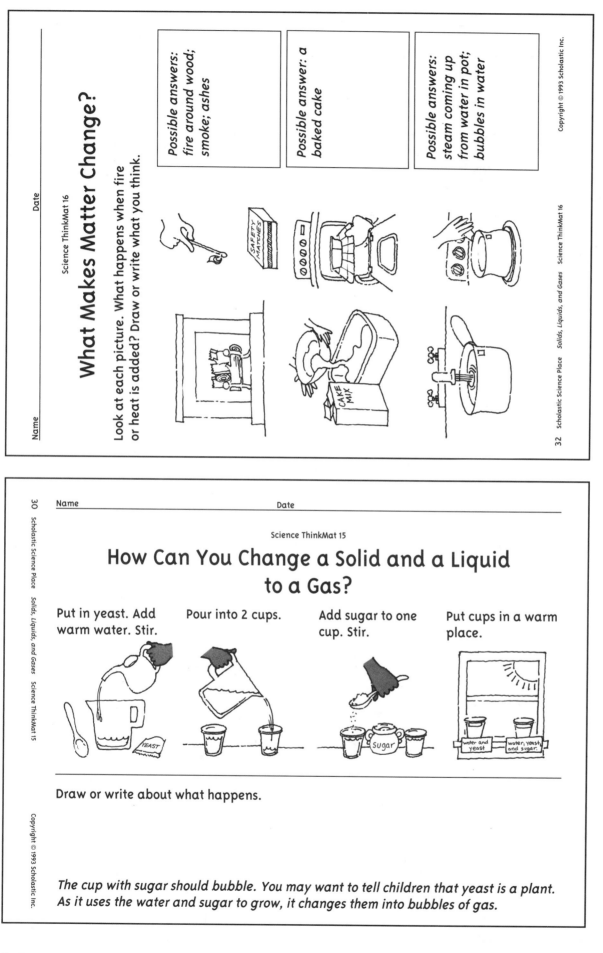

Science ThinkMat 16

What Makes Matter Change?

Look at each picture. What happens when fire or heat is added? Draw or write what you think.

Possible answers: fire around wood; smoke; ashes

Possible answer: a baked cake

Possible answers: steam coming up from water in pot; bubbles in water

---

Name   Date

Science ThinkMat 15

How Can You Change a Solid and a Liquid to a Gas?

Put in yeast. Add warm water. Stir.

Pour into 2 cups.

Add sugar to one cup. Stir.

Put cups in a warm place.

Draw or write about what happens.

The cup with sugar should bubble. You may want to tell children that yeast is a plant. As it uses the water and sugar to grow, it changes them into bubbles of gas.

Science ThinkMat 18

What Did We Learn?

Circle the best answer.

1. Which is a solid?

2. Which takes the shape of its container?

3. Circle the shape that shows matter changing form to another.

Science ThinkMat 17

Where Can You Find Changing Matter?

Color the matter that is changing. Then put a ○ around the solids, a □ around the liquids, and a △ around the gases.

Answers will vary.